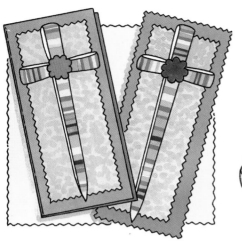
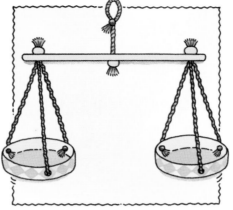
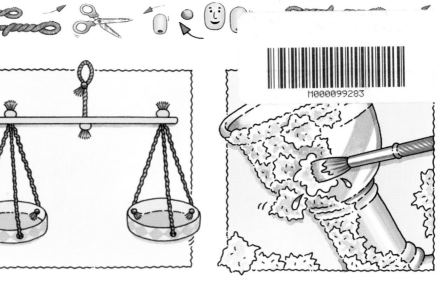
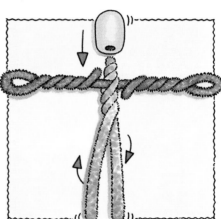

EASTER MAKE & DO

Gillian Chapman

Reproducible Bible
Craft Ideas for
Ages 6–12

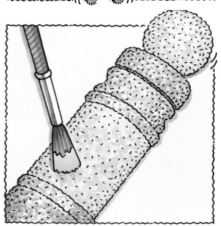

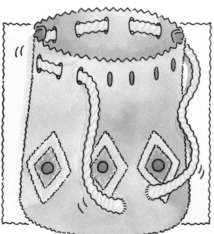

CONCORDIA PUBLISHING HOUSE · SAINT LOUIS

HOW TO USE THIS BOOK

You will find within this book a wealth of ideas and inspiration that you'll love using with children at home or in the classroom.

These creative ideas are great for celebrating Holy Week and Easter as well as fun, hands-on ways to bring New Testament stories to life. And not a fluffy bunny in sight!

Craft ideas vary from simple to the more challenging, and each one is designed to be made with inexpensive supplies using recycled materials where possible. Children will experience the thrill of making something wonderful almost "out of nothing."

To help keep preparation time to a minimum, each project spread features:

✳ a lively retelling of the Bible story, suitable for reading aloud

✳ a list of materials needed

✳ clear, step-by-step instructions

✳ a photograph of how the finished article may look.

Ideal for children in first through sixth grades, these crafts will appeal to all ages and interests.

All the craft ideas were designed and tested by Gillian Chapman, a well-known author of craft books. Drawing on her wide experience leading children's workshops on arts and crafts, Gillian includes helpful tips and safety recommendations on the pages that follow. It will

be helpful for you to read this section before you begin.

Part of the excitement and satisfaction of *Make and Do* crafts is when children express their creativity and develop an original slant on an idea or design, whatever the results! Some children (and adults, let's face it) may struggle to follow instructions and lose interest very quickly if they feel an activity is too difficult. Bearing that in mind, most of the projects in this book can be modified according to an individual's ability. For example, where sewing is involved, you may use craft glue instead; where drawing is involved, you may cut pictures out of magazines.

You will find reproducible patterns in the middle of this book as a helpful starting point. Some of these can be enlarged to produce wall-sized pictures, collages, or displays for bedrooms, classrooms, or churches.

Specific projects, such as the cup or the money-lenders' scales, could be used as props for school or church drama productions. Having read the Bible story and made the crafts, children can enjoy the further dimension of bringing a story to life themselves through drama. The Easter diorama may also be used to reenact the story.

There are endless possibilities for using *Easter Make and Do* to explore God's Holy Word and discover His salvation promise fulfilled in Jesus. Enjoy them!

CONTENTS

BIBLE CRAFT TIPS
Additional practical information

Safety First

All tools and equipment must be used with care and respect! Sharp pencils, scissors, and needles can all be dangerous if used incorrectly.

An adult will need to help with carpentry tools and cutting tools.

If you need to use a craft knife, be sure you also use a cutting board.

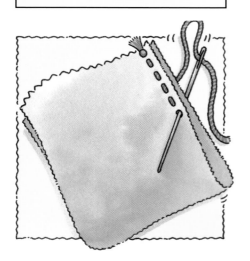

Paints

Poster or craft paints are great for painting on paper and cardstock and for painting models made from paper pulp and papier-mâché. They come in many colors including metallics. Acrylic paints are better to paint wooden surfaces.

Paints can be mixed on a palette or paper plate. Keep a jar of clean water on hand to clean brushes. Change the water frequently to keep colors looking bright.

For detailed drawings of animals, figures, and faces sketch in the outlines first with pencil, then color in using colored pencils. If you have a set of watercolor paints and a fine brush, use these instead.

Shaped Scissors

Special scissors with a shaped cutting edge are available for craftwork. Use these, or pinking shears, to give paper and fabric a fun patterned edge. They're especially effective for the palm cross card and the fish hanging.

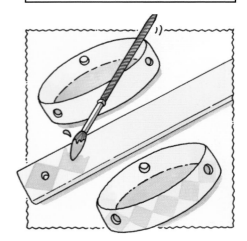

Glues

Craft glue is perfect for most craft projects. It can be diluted for papier-mâché projects. It will stick paper, card, and most fabrics – but in most cases it must be used very sparingly. It will wash off with cold water.

Glue sticks are better for neat finishes, but work only on paper and thin card.

When using craft glue to do fine work, such as gluing beads and sequins onto fabric, use glue in a bottle with a fine tip. If you don't have such a container, then pour some of the glue into a small plastic container (like a lid) and use a toothpick to put tiny blobs of glue where it's needed.

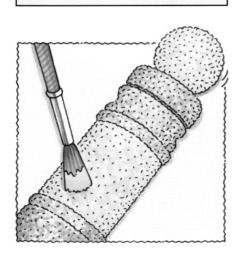

Keeping Clean

Make sure all work surfaces are protected with newspaper and all clothing is covered with a paint smock, an old shirt, or an apron. Keep paper towels or an old towel handy for easy clean-ups.

Brushes

Keep separate brushes for painting and gluing. Always clean them in warm soapy water after each use and let them air dry before putting them away.

JESUS ENTERS JERUSALEM

Here comes the King!

Matthew 21:1–11; Mark 11:1–10; Luke 19:29–38; John 12:12–15

Jesus and His disciples were going to Jerusalem for the Passover festival.

Jesus sent two of His disciples ahead, saying, "Go to the village over there where you will find a young donkey. Bring it to me. Say that the Lord needs it."

The two friends found the donkey, put their cloaks over the donkey's back, and brought it to Jesus.

Just as the prophets had foretold, Jesus rode into the great city of Jerusalem.

Huge crowds came to greet Jesus, spreading their cloaks on the road and waving palm branches.

"Hosanna!" they shouted which means "Lord save us."

They cheered and waved to Jesus, their Savior, who would soon die for the sins of all people. They cheered and waved to Jesus, their heavenly King, who came to Jerusalem riding on a donkey.

1 For the crosses, measure and mark strips 3/4" wide by 15" long on the wrapping paper. You will need two strips for each cross. Carefully cut out the strips using the scissors.

You will need:

✂

Thin colored cardstock

Scraps of construction paper

Wrapping paper

Scissors

Glue stick

Ruler and pencil

Shaped scissors or pinking shears

Stickers, over 3/4" in size, such as hearts, stars, circles

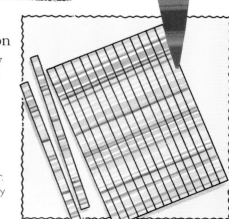

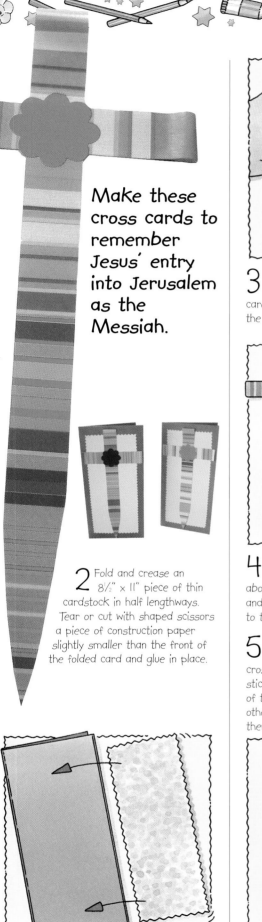

Make these cross cards to remember Jesus' entry into Jerusalem as the Messiah.

2 Fold and crease an 8½" x 11" piece of thin cardstock in half lengthways. Tear or cut with shaped scissors a piece of construction paper slightly smaller than the front of the folded card and glue in place.

3 Make the crosses by taking one of the paper strips and folding it in half, being careful to not crease along the fold. Pinch the strip with your fingers as shown above.

4 Take a second strip and cut it in half. Hold one half across the first strip about a quarter of the way from the top and use a sticker to stick the second strip to the first.

5 Fold each end of the second strip so they meet in the back to make the cross. Stick them in place with another sticker at the back. If you use two stickers of the same shape, they will stick to each other and hold the cross in place between them.

6 Use the scissors to trim the long ends of the cross into a point. With the glue stick, glue the cross to the front of the card. Make the bookmark in a similar way, but use a narrow strip cut from another piece of cardstock.

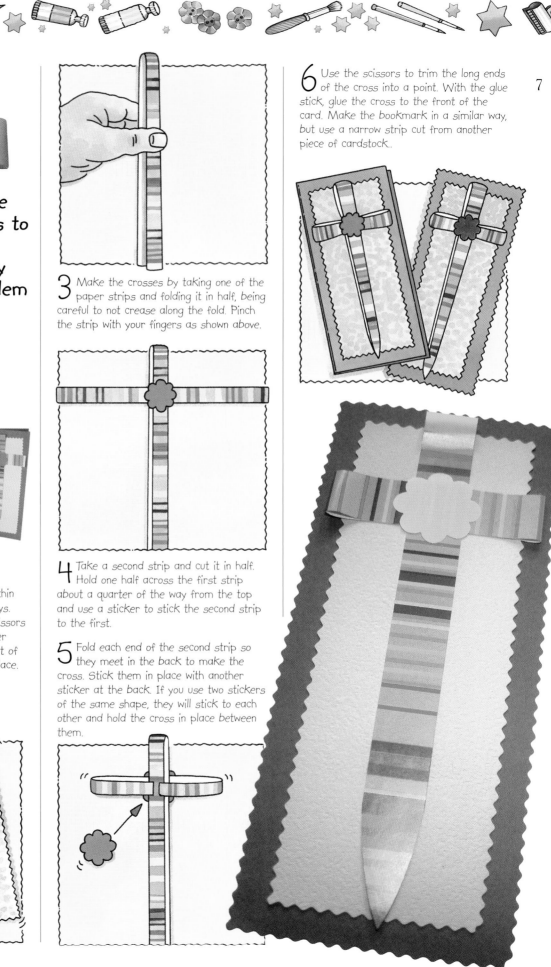

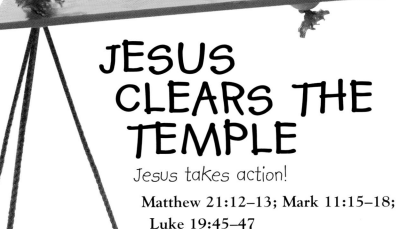

JESUS CLEARS THE TEMPLE

Jesus takes action!

Matthew 21:12–13; Mark 11:15–18; Luke 19:45–47

While Jesus was in Jerusalem, He went to the temple. God's house was a place to pray in this noisy, bustling city.

But when Jesus entered the temple courtyard, He saw people buying and selling animals and doves, and other people cheating as they changed money. The temple had become a noisy, smelly market place, just like the rest of the city.

Jesus took action. He drove out the money changers and turned over the tables.

"You are turning My house into a den of robbers!" shouted Jesus. "It should be a house of prayer for all people!"

You will need:

✂

A small round wooden or cardboard box

Scissors (and some adult help)

Ruler

16" x 1½" balsa wood strip

Poster or craft paints and brush

7 lengths of string, cord, or yarn

Tapestry needle

3 large wooden beads

1 Ask an adult to help you make three equally spaced holes in the rims of the lid and bottom of the round box, using the sharp point of the scissors.

2 Using the ruler to position them accurately, ask an adult to help you make three holes in the balsa wood strip, again using the point of the scissors. Make a hole exactly in the center of the strip and one hole 1" from each end.

Jesus wanted people to keep the temple a holy place. Jesus' actions and words made some people afraid and angry. The chief priests and teachers of the law saw Jesus as a threat and began to make plans to kill Him. But although leaders plotted against Jesus, He kept doing His Father's will.

Make scales like the money-lenders' used in the temple courts.

3 Paint the lid and base of the box and the balsa wood strip. Money-lenders' scales would have been made from metal, but you can paint your scales with bright colors and patterns.

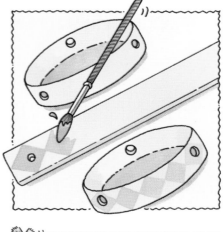

4 Thread a length of string through each of the three holes in the lid of the box and tie a knot at the end of each string. Use the tapestry needle to thread the three strings through the hole in the end of the strip. Thread the strings through a bead, then tie the ends together.

5 Do the same thing to attach the base of the box to the other end of the strip. Thread the needle with the last piece of string and tie a knot in the end of the string. Thread it through a bead, then through the center hole and tie a loop in the end.

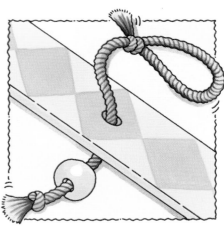

6 If you have measured the string equally and made your scales accurately, they should be evenly balanced when you hold them up by the center string. Use small coins as weights and use your scales to weigh small pieces of fruit, nuts, or candy.

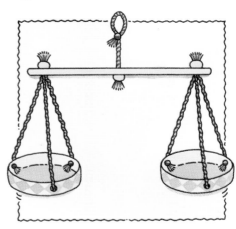

JESUS IS ANOINTED
The smell of perfume fills the room

Matthew 26:6–13; Mark 14:3–9

Shortly before Passover, Jesus went to eat at a friend's house. A woman named Mary came up to Jesus, holding a small but very precious alabaster jar.

When Mary opened the jar, the sweet smell of perfume wafted out. Mary had brought a very expensive gift for Jesus. To show her devotion for Jesus, she poured it over His head. This custom was common at feasts and was called "anointing."

"What's she doing?" asked some of Jesus' disciples. "That's a waste of money, just pouring it away like that!"

Jesus heard them complaining and said, "Leave her alone. She has done a beautiful thing. She has prepared My body for burial."

You will need:

✂

Small glass jar with screw-top lid, such as a spice or herb jar

Paper towels

Ping-Pong ball

Craft glue and brush

Paints and brush

Metallic craft paints

Small beads, needle and thread for decoration

Remove the lid from the clean glass jar and brush the top with craft glue. Tear up small pieces of paper towel and stick them to the surface. Avoid gluing the paper to the screw top rim.

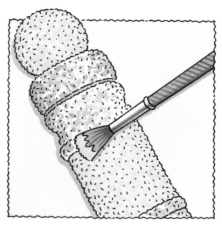

2 Cover the entire surface of the jar, making sure the paper remains crinkly. Cover the lid, Keeping it separate from the jar. Allow to dry. Add more layers to give an extra crinkly texture to the surface.

4 When the jar and lid are completely dry, paint them both. The perfume jar that Mary used was made of alabaster and would have looked very plain, but you can decorate your perfume jar to make it very special. Allow to dry.

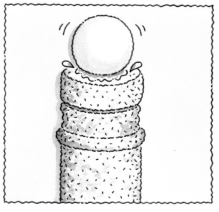

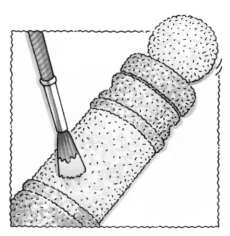

3 Glue the Ping-Pong ball to the top of the lid and cover it with the glued paper towel so it has a crinkly texture to match the jar.

5 To make the jar look very expensive, paint a thin coat of gold or silver paint sparingly over the surface, making sure the first color still shows through.

Make this jar to remind you of Mary's gift to Jesus.

6 Finally, decorate the perfume jar. Thread very small beads onto a length of thread and tie Knots in the ends. Wind the thread of beads around the jar and glue them firmly in place.

JESUS IS BETRAYED

Judas betrays Jesus for thirty silver coins

Matthew 26:14–16; Mark 14:10–11; Luke 22:3–6

The chief priests wanted to get rid of Jesus. But they didn't know how to capture Him.

Judas Iscariot, who had been one of Jesus' closest friends, did not love Jesus or want to serve Him. Instead, he did something evil.

Judas went to the chief priests and asked, "What will you pay me if I hand Jesus over to you?"

"We'll give you thirty pieces of silver," they said.

After that, Judas watched for a chance to hand Jesus over to them. Jesus knew what Judas had done, but it did not change His love for all people. Jesus would still suffer and die for the sins of all.

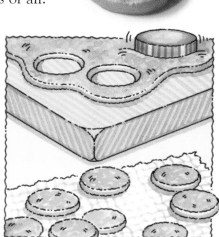

You will need:

✂

TO MAKE THE COINS

Self-hardening clay

Rolling pin and wooden or plastic board

Toothpicks

Carving tools

Round plastic bottle top

Sheets of paper towels

Silver craft paint and brush

TO MAKE THE MONEY BAG

6" x 12" piece of felt

Needle, thread, and scissors

16" length of cord

Scraps of felt and beads

1 Using the rolling pin, roll out the clay on the board to an even thickness of about ¼".

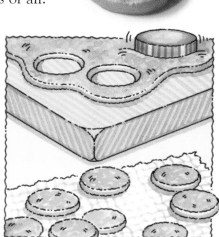

2 Use the round plastic lid as a cutter to cut 30 circles from the clay. Carefully remove these clay circles from the board and place them on the paper towel.

Make these silver coins as a reminder of how Judas turned against Jesus.

5 Coins were often kept safe in small money bags made from leather or cloth. To make the bag, fold the piece of felt in half and sew along each side using a short, simple, running stitch.

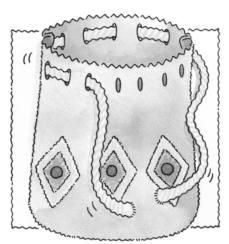

6 Turn the bag inside out so the stitching is on the inside. Glue on scraps of felt and beads to decorate the bag. Ask an adult to use the scissors to make a row of small holes about ¾" from the top. Thread the cord in and out of the holes. Thread a small bead on to each end and tie a knot. Fray the ends, then tie the ends together. Keep your silver coins in the money bag and pull the cord tight to keep them safe.

3 Use the toothpicks or tools to decorate the clay circles, making them look like coins. Roman coins were often decorated with the head of the emperor, but you can make your own designs. Try to keep the coins flat and allow them to dry out completely—about one day.

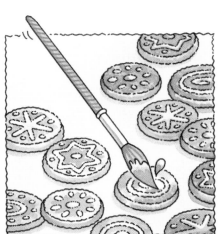

4 When the coins are dry, paint them silver. Paint one side and let dry before turning over to paint the reverse side.

JESUS WASHES HIS DISCIPLES' FEET

Jesus shows His disciples how much He loves them

John 13:1–17

Jesus knew He would soon die and would not be with His friends much longer. He wanted to celebrate the Passover meal with them one last time. Passover was a special time of remembering how God had rescued Moses and the Israelites from slavery in Egypt many years ago.

Jesus met His 12 friends at the upper room of a house.

He took a bowl of water and began to wash His disciples' feet.

"You mustn't wash my feet!" said Peter. "You are our Master, not our servant!"

"Unless I wash you, you don't belong to Me," said Jesus.

"Then wash my hands and head as well!" said Peter.

Jesus washed Peter's feet.

"Now that I have washed your feet," said Jesus, "you must also wash one another's feet. Do loving tasks for one another as I have done for you." Jesus' life of service continued to the cross where He died for the sins of all people.

You will need:

✂

Large plastic bowl

Newspaper

Craft glue and brush

Plastic wrap and cooking oil

Light brown paint and brush

Scissors

Pictures cut from magazines

Pencil

Spray shellac (optional)

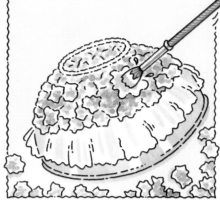

1 Use the plastic bowl as your mold. Lightly grease the outside with the oil and cover with the plastic wrap. Cover the outside of the bowl with six layers of small newspaper pieces glued with diluted glue. The design of this papier-mâché bowl is shallow, so you will only need to cover about 8" up the sides.

2 Allow the papier-mâché to dry overnight, then remove it from the plastic bowl by pulling-away the plastic wrap. Neaten the bowl by trimming around the edges with the scissors.

3 Neaten the edge of the bowl further by gluing small strips of newspaper around the rim. Allow to dry.

4 When it is dry, paint the bowl inside and out with a light brown paint to make the bowl look as if it is made from clay. Decorate the bowl with a simple mosaic pattern. Draw an outline in pencil around the rim of the bowl and include a small design in the center.

5 Cut out lots of small squares from the colored pages of magazines and arrange all the squares into groups of similar colors to make the mosaics. This design does not cover the bowl completely, but makes a border pattern and center design.

6 Follow the pencil guidelines and glue the paper squares to the surface of the bowl. Build up the mosaic pattern and overlap the squares if necessary. When you have finished decorating the bowl, you can varnish it to help strengthen and protect the mosaic.

Make this mosaic bowl and think about how much Jesus loved His friends.

DIORAMA FIGURES

You will need:

✂️

TO MAKE THE FIGURES

Chenille Sticks

Scissors

Scraps of colored fabric, felt, and yarn

Wooden beads for heads

Thin black felt-tipped pen

Pieces of thin cardstock

Tape

Paper towel

Craft glue and glue brush

Paint and brush

Toothpicks

TO MAKE THE SWORDS, CLUBS, AND TORCHES

Scraps of gray or silver cardstock

Paper towel

Paint and brush

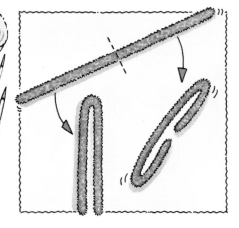

1 Make the basic structure of all the figures by bending and twisting two chenille sticks as shown.

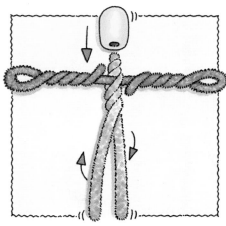

2 Attach a bead to the top as a head. Wrap the "arms" with yarn.

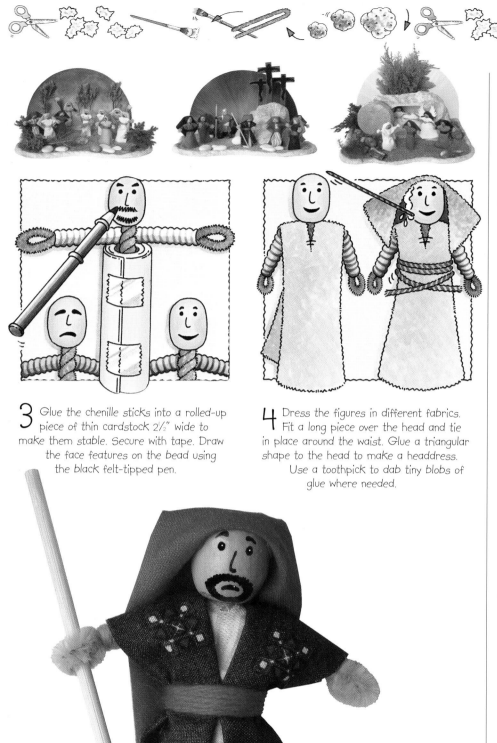

3 Glue the chenille sticks into a rolled-up piece of thin cardstock 2½" wide to make them stable. Secure with tape. Draw the face features on the bead using the black felt-tipped pen.

4 Dress the figures in different fabrics. Fit a long piece over the head and tie in place around the waist. Glue a triangular shape to the head to make a headdress. Use a toothpick to dab tiny blobs of glue where needed.

Some of the figures hold swords, clubs, torches, or sticks. Make the swords by cutting out small pieces of silver cardstock and glue together. Make the torches and clubs by twisting pieces of glued paper towel together and molding to make the shapes. Then paint them. Attach the weapons and sticks by pushing them through the pipe cleaner loops at the ends of the arms.

DIORAMA FIGURES

JESUS DIES ON A CROSS
Pages 26-27

JESUS IS ALIVE!
Pages 28-29

You will need:

✂

TO MAKE THE SOLDIER
2 large buttons
Scraps of foil
Scraps of felt
Toothpick

TO MAKE THE ANGEL
Large button
Brown and yellow yarn
Scraps of gray or silver card
Scraps of white fabric

TO MAKE THE GRAVE CLOTHES
White paper towel
Scraps of white fabric

For the Roman soldier, thread two button feet onto the chenille stick legs. Tie felt leggings around his legs and attach a felt cloak across his body. Make his helmet from small pieces of aluminum foil shaped to fit the bead head. Add toothpick spear as shown.

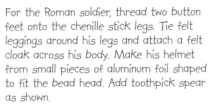

To give the angels a seated shape, thread a button through the pipe cleaner legs as shown. Make hair from lengths of brown yarn glued across the bead head.

Cut out wings from silver cardstock (see pattern) and attach to the back of the figure with yellow yarn. Dress the angels with garments made from white fabric.

The grave clothes were left in the tomb when Jesus rose from the dead. Make the body shroud from lengths of glued white paper towel, wrapped to make a cocoon shape. The head cloth is a piece of white fabric folded together.

PATTERNS

JESUS DIES
ON A CROSS
Pages 26-27

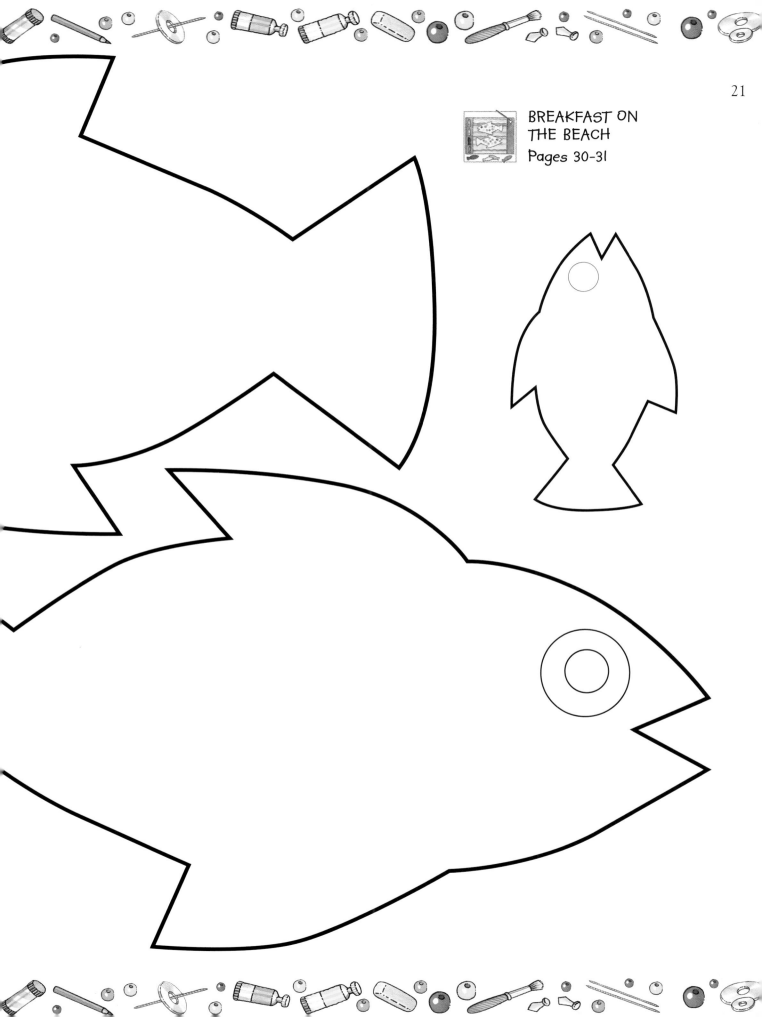

BREAKFAST ON
THE BEACH
Pages 30-31

THE LAST SUPPER

Jesus shares a special meal with His disciples

Matthew 26:17–30; Mark 14:17–26; Luke 22:14–20

After Jesus had finished washing everyone's feet, He reclined at the table with His disciples, ready to eat the Passover meal.

Jesus said, "One of you is going to hand Me over to be killed."

"Surely not I!" each one said to another.

You will need:

✂

2 clean plastic dessert bowls

Plastic spool

Scissors

Dried beans, peas, and lentils

Paper towel

Tape

Craft glue and brush

Toothpick

Silver or brown paint

Paintbrush

Make this special cup to remember Jesus' words at the Last Supper.

But Jesus already knew it would be Judas Iscariot.

Jesus took the cup of wine, thanked God for it, and offered it to them. "Drink from it, all of you. Do this to remember Me," said Jesus. "This is My blood, for many." Jesus' friends drank the wine.

Then He took the bread, gave thanks, broke it, and gave it to His friends. "Take and eat. Do this to remember Me," said Jesus. "This is My body." The disciples ate the bread.

They sang a song together, then went to the Mount of Olives.

It wouldn't be long until Jesus' body and blood would be sacrificed on the cross for the sins of all people. Today, Jesus gives us His body and blood in Holy Communion

1 Use the scissors carefully to cut out the bottom section of one of the dessert bowls to form the base of the cup. Tip this upside-down, as shown below. The spool will form the stem of the cup.

2 Glue the spool between the two sections and allow to dry.

3 Brush the surface with glue and cover the bowls with torn pieces of paper towel. The layers of paper towel will help to hold the two plastic bowls and the spool together. Make sure the paper remains nice and crinkly. Cover the whole surface inside and out with at least two layers of paper and allow to dry.

4 Wind yarn or string around the rim of the cup, fixing the string in place with dabs of glue. Then glue string around the stem and the base of the cup and allow to dry.

5 Make a raised pattern on the surface of the cup with dried beans, peas, and lentils. Place small blobs of glue on the surface using the toothpick to carefully position the beans on the glue.

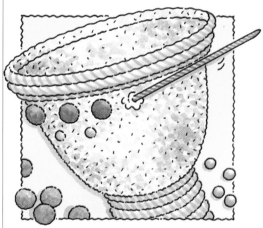

6 When you have finished decorating the cup, allow the glue to dry completely. Then paint the cup inside and out with the silver or brown poster paint. It is likely that the cup Jesus used would have been made of earthenware. Today the cups used for the Lord's Supper in church are usually made of silver.

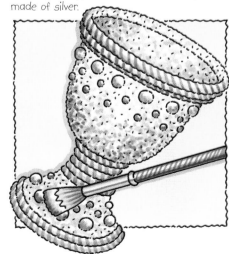

23

24

JESUS IS ARRESTED
The Garden of Gethsemane

Matthew 26:36–56; Mark 14:32–50; Luke 22:39–53

On the Mount of Olives was a garden called Gethsemane. Here Jesus knelt to pray to His Father. He knew that the time was coming for Him to be taken away.

Jesus asked His disciples to pray with Him. But they kept falling asleep. "Why are you sleeping?" He asked. "Watch and pray with Me."

Suddenly a crowd of soldiers and others sent by the chief priests and Jewish leaders came toward them with torches, clubs, and swords. Judas led the group and came up to Jesus to kiss Him. This showed the soldiers where Jesus was.

One of Jesus' disciples took out a sword and in his fear chopped off the ear of the high priest's servant.

"Put that sword away," said Jesus. "All who use the sword will die by the sword. Things must happen in this way."

Then Jesus touched the servant's ear and healed it.

Jesus was then arrested and taken away to the high priest.

It was the time when the powers of evil would try to defeat God's plan to save all people. But Jesus arose to victory on Easter.

You will need:

✂

TO MAKE THE BASE AND BACKDROP

Corrugated cardboard 16" x 12" for the base

Pencil and scissors

Thick cardstock 16" x 10" for the backdrop

Compass

Paper towel, craft glue and glue brush

Paints and brush

Small pieces of greenery and foliage

Florists' oasis

Sand and small rocks or gravel

To assemble this diorama you will need Jesus, the disciples, Judas, the guards, and onlookers, using the directions on pages 16–19.

1 Draw a random shape on the cardboard, leaving one side straight. Cut out the shape with the scissors. Glue a strip of crumpled newspaper around the edge of the card to form a ridge, then cover with pieces of glued paper towel. Allow to dry, then paint to resemble rocks and stones. Decorate with sand and small sized gravel, small pieces of greenery and foliage, pushed into clay or florists' oasis.

Make this diorama scene and recreate the drama in the Garden of Gethsemane.

2 Draw an arc or semi-circle on the cardstock with the compass, then carefully cut it out. Paint it to look like the night sky in garden. Position the backdrop behind the scene base. Glue in place and prop it up with a suitable weight (e.g. a couple of soup cans).

3 Directions for making the figures for this diorama are on pages 16-19.

JESUS DIES ON A CROSS

The people shout, "Crucify Him!"

Matthew 27:11–50; Mark 15:1–38;
Luke 23:33–46; John 19:1–30

Jesus was brought before Pilate, the Roman governor. "What has this man done wrong?" Pilate asked the crowd.

"He is causing trouble," said the chief priests. "He says He is a king."

"Are You the King of the Jews?" asked Pilate.

"Yes, it is as you say," said Jesus.

"What shall I do with Jesus?" Pilate asked the crowd.

"Crucify Him!" they shouted. "Put Him on a cross to die!"

Pilate did not think Jesus had done anything wrong. But he wanted to please the crowd so he handed Jesus over to the soldiers to be taken to a place called Golgotha. There He was nailed to a cross. Above His head was a sign saying: The King of the Jews.

It was a terrible day. Jesus' mother, Mary, stood close by and watched and wept.

At midday, darkness came over the land and stayed until the middle of the afternoon. Then Jesus cried out in a loud voice to God, and breathed His last breath.

The saving work Jesus had come to earth to do was completed. Through His perfect life, Jesus, the Savior of the world, defeated sin, death, and the devil.

You will need:

TO MAKE THE MOUND AND CROSSES

Newspaper

Tape

Thick cardstock for the crosses

Corrugated cardboard for the base

Scissors

Paper towel

Craft glue and glue brush

Paints and brush

Sand and small stones or gravel

1 To make the figures (four women, two men, and a Roman soldier) turn to pages 16 to 19 for full instructions.

2 First make a base for the mound by cutting a random shape from the cardboard. Then crumple up balls of newspaper and tape them to the base to make the basic height, form, and shape of the mound. Tape all the balls of newspaper together to make a firm structure.

Make this dramatic diorama of the events of Good Friday.

3 Cover the newspaper mound with glue. Take a square of paper towel, wet it with water, squeeze out the excess water, and drape it over the newspaper, making sure it stays nice and crinkly. Cover the mound with more glue and pieces of wet paper towel until all the newspaper is completely covered with the textured surface.

4 Allow to dry and then paint the mound to resemble a rock. Use light brown paint to cover the surface then, when dry, brush on gray paint to get a realistic effect.

5 Make the three crosses from strips of cardstock, 3" x 1" and 6" x 1", glued together, then painted. Use the pattern on page 20 to cut the figures from black felt and glue them to the crosses. Carefully use the tips of the scissors to make three slots in the mound and then slide the crosses into position.

6 Make or reuse the base from page 24. Make a new backdrop and paint it with dramatic colors. Position the mound and crosses on the tray. Assemble the diorama as shown.

JESUS IS ALIVE!

God raises Jesus from death

Matthew 27:57–28:10; Mark 16:1–18;
Luke 24:1–10

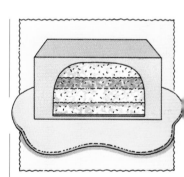

Jesus' body was taken from the cross and put in a tomb. A large stone was rolled in front to block the entrance.

Three days passed. All Jesus' friends were sad and weeping.

Then, early on Sunday morning, some of the women went to His tomb with special spices to anoint His body. But what a shock they had when they got there! The large stone had been rolled away! Inside the tomb, Jesus' body was gone. Suddenly two angels in bright shining clothes appeared.

"Don't look for Jesus here," they said. "He's risen, just as He said... Go quickly and tell His disciples."

The women couldn't believe it! They ran home at once and told Jesus' disciples that He was alive!

You will need:

Small cardboard box
(e.g., small shoe or
pasta box)

Small rectangular box
(e.g., toothpaste box)

Plastic lid
or saucer large
enough to
cover tomb entrance

Newspaper

Tape

Corrugated cardboard
for base

Scissors

Paper towel

Craft glue and glue brush

Paints and brush

Small pieces of
greenery and foliage

Modeling clay
or florists' oasis

Sand and small
stones or gravel

Make this Easter garden diorama and thank God for raising Jesus from death.

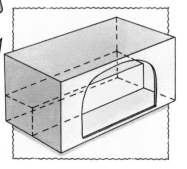

1 Draw an arch shape on one side of the larger box to represent the tomb entrance and cut it out. Glue the smaller box to the inside of the larger box to make the ledge inside the tomb.

2 Cover all the inside surfaces of the box with glued pieces of paper towel to give a textured surface all over. Place the box on a piece of cardboard and draw a shape around the box, leaving 4" to the front and 2" on the sides of the box. Cut out the shape and glue the box to the cardboard.

3 Use crumpled balls of newspaper to build up the cave shape to the sides and top of the box. Hold the newspaper in place with tape. Then using the same method described to make the mound on page 26, cover the newspaper with glue and drape pieces of wet paper towel over the structure to make it look like a cave tomb.

4 Make a groove in front of the tomb for the stone to roll along. Build up the two sides of the groove with lengths of crumpled newspaper, held in place with pieces of glued paper towel.

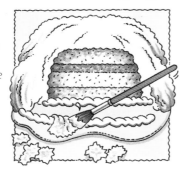

5 Make the rolling stone by covering the plastic lid with glued paper towel as described earlier. Paint the tomb and the rolling stone to look like rock.

7 Assemble the diorama using a base and backdrop as shown on page 24. Paint the backdrop with golden rays. Use fresh foliage, gravel, and small stones to decorate the garden.

8 To make the figures (two women, two angels, and Jesus) turn to pages 16 to 19 for full instructions.

JESUS PROVIDES BREAKFAST

The risen Jesus appears to His disciples
John 21:1–14

Over the next few days, Jesus appeared to His disciples, showing them that He really was alive.

One night, Peter and a group of disciples were out fishing in their boat. They had caught nothing. Early the next morning, Jesus stood on the shore, watching them. He was far away, so they couldn't see at first who it was.

"Friends haven't you caught any fish?" He shouted to the fishermen.

"No!" they said.

"Then throw your net on the other side of the boat," said Jesus. "You will catch fish!"

They did as He said and sure enough, their nets were filled with wriggling fish.

"It's the Lord!" said Peter. They knew that only Jesus could do something so amazing. Peter was so excited that he jumped out of the boat and swam to shore.

Jesus had made a small fire on the shore. He was ready to cook some of the fish. He had some bread for them too. His disciples sat with Him and ate breakfast on the beach.

Just as Jesus provided help and food for His disciples that day, He would continue to provide for all their needs—both on earth and in heaven. He provides the same things for us too in His Word and the Sacraments.

You will need:

14" x 20" piece of pale blue felt

Black felt tipped pen

Scraps of colored felt, fabric, and netting

Craft glue and brush

White cardstock and pencil

Scissors

Buttons, beads, and trimmings for decoration

Toothpicks

24" length of wooden dowel

Self hardening clay

Draw one large and one small fish shape on the cardstock. You could use the outlines on pages 20–21. Cut the card shapes out carefully.

Fish are a symbol for Jesus. Make this wall hanging to show that you *believe* in Jesus.

5 Cut two strips of fabric to fit along the two sides of the hanging and glue these in place. Then glue the small fish on top of these strips to make the border patterns. If you have any small buttons or beads, use them to decorate the fish.

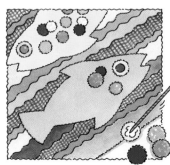

6 Cut four strips of fabric to make loops along the top of the hanging and glue in place. Thread the wooden dowel through the loops. Make two clay balls. Push a clay ball on each end of the dowel to hold the hanging in place. Paint the clay balls after they are dry.

2 Lay the fish patterns on the fabric, draw around them with the felt-tipped pen, and cut them out. You will need two large fish and eight small ones. If you have a selection of fabrics, use different colors and patterns.

3 Cut several wavy strips of colored fabric and glue them across the background to make an underwater scene. Use blue, gray, and green netting and wavy trimmings. Don't worry about lining up the ends of the wavy strips along the two sides as these will be covered by the border pattern.

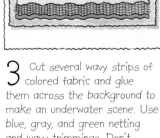

4 Glue the two large fish to the center of the scene, on the top of the waves. Cut out several fabric circles and glue them to the bodies of the fish to represent their scales.

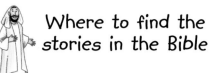

Where to find the stories in the Bible

Jesus enters Jerusalem:
Matthew 21:1-11; Mark 11:1-10;
Luke 19:29-38; John 12:12-15

Jesus clears the temple:
Matthew 21:12-13; Mark 11:15-18; Luke 19:45-47

Jesus is anointed:
Matthew 26:6-13; Mark 14:3-9

Jesus is betrayed:
Matthew 26:14-16; Mark 14:10-1; Luke 22:3-6

Jesus washes His disciples' feet:
John 13:1-17

The Last Supper:
Matthew 26:17-30; Mark 14:17-26; Luke 22:14-20

Jesus is arrested:
Matthew 26:36-56; Mark 14:32-50;
Luke 22:39-53

Jesus dies on a cross:
Matthew 27:11-50; Mark 15:1-38; Luke 23:33-46;
John 19:1-30

Jesus is alive!:
Matthew 27:57-28:10; Mark 16:1-8;
Luke 24:1-10

Jesus provides breakfast:
John 21:1-14

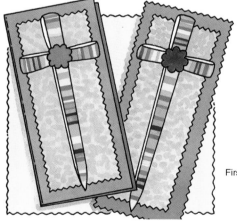

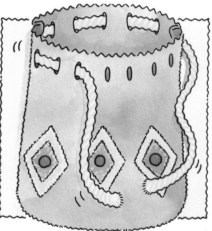

This edition published by Concordia Publishing House
3558 S. Jefferson Ave., St. Louis, MO 63118-3968
ISBN 0-7586-0583-8

Published in the UK by
The Bible Reading Fellowship
First Floor, Elsfield Hall, 15-17 Elsfield Way, Oxford OX2 8FG
ISBN 1 84101 348 X

First edition 2004

Editorial Director Annette Reynolds
Project Editor Leena Lane
Art Director Gerald Rogers
Pre-production Krystyna Hewitt
Production John Laister

British Library Cataloguing in Publication Data.
A catalogue record for this book is available from
the British Library.

This material can be photocopied, duplicated or
enlarged for individual or group use.

Printed and bound in Singapore

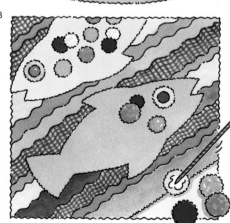

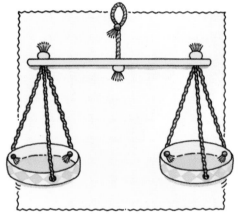